BOOK ONE

THE RHINEGOLD

Adapted by Roy Thomas ▫ Art by Gil Kane

Color Art by Jim Woodring ▫ Lettered by John Costanza

IN THE DAY-SPRING OF THE AGES, THERE WAS NEITHER SEA NOR SHORE, HEAVEN NOR EARTH, BUT ONLY A VAST, YAWNING ABYSS...

...BOUNDED ON THE ONE SIDE BY HEAT AND FLAME...

...ON THE OTHER BY FREEZING MISTS.

AS FIRE MET ICE, ABOVE THE VOID, WARMED DROPS OF MOISTURE BEGAN TO FALL INTO THE GAPING CHASM.

OVER TIME, THE DROPS QUICKENED, HARDENED...

IN DAYS SOON AFTER WERE MAN AND WOMAN MADE, BY WOTAN AND HIS BROTHERS HONER AND LODUR, FROM SPLINTERS OF WOOD THEY FOUND FLOATING UPON THE WATER.

FROM THIS PAIR ARE DESCENDED ALL THE HUMAN RACE, WHOSE HABITATION IS CALLED MIDGARD.

THEN DID WOTAN AND HIS NEW RACE OF GODS SET THEIR EYES UPON THE HEIGHTS, WHERE THEY WOULD RAISE A HALL OF THE VALIANT, TO WHICH THE BRAVEST OF HUMAN WARRIORS WOULD BE TAKEN WHEN SLAIN IN BATTLE.

AND TO THE RIVER RHINE, WHICH FLOWS GREEN AS EMERALDS TOWARD THE SEA THAT CIRCLES THE WORLD, WOTAN CONSIGNED A HOARD OF GOLD WHOSE MAGIC EVEN HE COULD NEVER FULLY MASTER.

THUS ARE TIME'S BEGINNINGS AND ITS END INEXTRICABLY ENTWINED.

FOR, BELOW THE RIVER'S WAVES, UNDULATING WATERS DO SLOWLY RESOLVE THEMSELVES INTO A CLOUD OF MIST WHICH GROWS EVER FINER AS IT DESCENDS...

...TILL, NEAR THE BOTTOM OF THE RHINE, A SPACE THE HEIGHT OF A MAN STANDS FREE AND DRY.

ABOVE THAT DARKENING GLOOM, THREE GRACEFUL FIGURES FLIT LIKE GLISTENING GODDESSES THROUGH THE WATERS.

THE RHINE-MAIDENS.

ROCK YE OUR CRADLE!

HO, MY WILD SISTERS--

ROLL, YE BILLOWS!

BADLY YOU GUARD THE SLEEPING GOLD, WOGLINDE.

WELLGUNDE! WATCH WITH MORE ZEAL, OR YOU'LL PAY FOR YOUR SPORTING!

AND YOU, DEAR FLOSSHILDE, WERE EVER TOO SERIOUS!

HELLO, BRIGHT NYMPHS!

HOW INVITING YOU LOOK!

FROM NIBELHEIM'S NIGHT I'D GLADLY COME NEAR, IF YOU'D BE KIND TO ME!

HEI! SOMEONE CALLS TO US!

FROM BELOW-- AMID THE SHADOWS!

FREIA'S CHARMS MEAN LITTLE TO US-- BUT IT MEANS *MUCH*, IF FROM YOU GODS WE REMOVE HER!

GOLDEN APPLES RIPEN IN HER GARDEN, BY HER HAND ALONE.

YOU, HER KINFOLK, EAT OF THEM--AND THEY ENDOW YOU WITH YOUTH EVER-LASTING.

LOGE-- WHY DO YOU NOT COME?

IF WE TAKE FREIA-- YOU'LL SWIFTLY *AGE*, AND *WASTE* TO NOTHING!

AYE! SO GIVE US YOUR ANSWER, WOTAN!

ASK SOME *OTHER* WAGE!

NO OTHER! FREIA FOLLOWS US, OR--

DONNER! FROH! SAVE ME FROM THESE *BEASTS*!

KRRAKKOOM

BACK, OVERBOLD ONES!

FROH'S *SWORD* SHIELDS HIS FAIR *SISTER*!

WE DESIRE NO *STRIFE*, YOU GODS.

BUT WE WANT OUR *DUE* REWARD!

OFT HAS *DONNER* DOLED OUT GIANTS THEIR DUE!

COME! MY *STORM-HAMMER* WILL PAY YOUR REWARD IN *FULL MEASURE*!

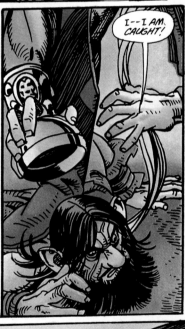

...WHEN YOU BUT LOOSEN MY HANDS.

BY SECRET COMMAND, THE NIBELUNGS ARE CALLED TO HIS PLACE.

ALREADY I CAN HEAR THEM COMING.

...THERE! THE PRICE IS PAID--NOW LET ME DEPART!

AND MY HELMET-- GIVE THAT TO ME, ALSO!

NAY! THE PLUNDER MUST PAY FOR THE PARDON.

ACCURSED THIEF!

PATIENCE, NIBELUNG! HE WHO MOLDED THAT HELM CAN MOLD ME ANOTHER!

ALBERICH NOW OWNS NOTHING AT ALL.

UNBIND, YOU TYRANTS, HIS BONDS!

OUGHT I TO FREE HIM, WOTAN?

ARE YOU NOW CONTENT?

A GOLDEN RING CIRCLES YOUR FINGER, GNOME...

HO! LET THE PILE BE MORE *TIGHTLY* PACKED!

I CAN STILL *SEE* THE GODDESS THROUGH THE CRANNIES.

COME! THIS GAP MUST BE *CLOSED!*

DO YOU WANT TO *MEASURE*, FAFNER?

THEN *MEASURE YOUR* STRENGTH AGAINST *MINE--!*

CALM YOURSELF! I THINK SHE IS FINALLY HIDDEN.

NAY! HER GOLDEN *HAIR* STILL SHINES THROUGH!

BUT THE *HOARD* IS SPENT...

THAT THING *YONDER*--THROW IT ON THE PILE!

EVEN...

...THE *TARNHELM*...?

MAKE HASTE, OR ELSE--

LET IT GO, ALSO.

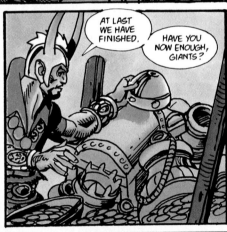

AT LAST WE HAVE FINISHED.

HAVE YOU NOW *ENOUGH*, GIANTS?

HOLD! HER EYES BEAM LIKE STARS UPON ME THROUGH THAT SINGLE CHINK!

WHILE I BEHOLD THOSE SWEET, SAD EYES, HOW CAN I EVER PART FROM HER?

AND ON *WOTAN'S* FINGER STILL GLEAMS A GOLDEN RING!

LET *THAT* CLOSE UP THE CREVICE!

TO ME, FREIA! YOU ARE... ...FREE.

MORE ON THE *MAID* THAN ON THE GOLD WERE YOUR EYES SET, BROTHER.

THUS IT IS ONLY FIT THAT MOST OF THE GOLD BE *MINE!*

LET HIM *HAVE* THE HOARD, FASOLT.

HOLD ON TO WHAT MATTERS -- *THE RING!*

HE'S *RIGHT!*

STAY BACK, FAFNER! *MINE* IS THE RING!

I LOST FOR IT FREIA'S SMILE!

NO!

THE RING IS MINE!

KRAKK

NOW, BROTHER--

--FEAST YOU *ONLY* UPON FREIA'S SMILE--

THUK

--FOR *NO MORE* SHALL YOU EVER TOUCH THE *RING!*